# The Bayeux Tapestry

## THE COMIC STRIP

Gilles Pivard / Arthur Shelton

It all began in 1064... from alliance to treason, via twists in the tale, lose yourself in this epic fresco and plunge into the very heart of the bloody Battle of Hastings on the 14th of October 1066, a date that was to go down in history... Join me in this epic adventure!

For a long time referred to as Queen Matilda's Tapestry, the Bayeux Tapestry is in fact a woollen embroidery on a 70 metre-long strip of linen.

Kept in the town's cathedral up to the 18th century, it was very probably commissioned to an English embroidery workshop, shortly after the conquest of England in 1066, by Bishop Odo of Conteville, William, Duke of Normandy's half brother.

Today, the Bayeux Tapestry offers a precious testimony to the Conquest of England and to this eventful period in history.

It is listed on UNESCO's Memory of the World Register.

KINGDOM
OF ENGLAND

■ LONDON

■ WINCHESTER

■ BOSHAM

■ HASTINGS

■ PEVENSEY

COUNTY OF
PONTHIEU

■ ROUEN

BAYEUX ■

■ CAEN

■ FALAISE

DUKEDOM OF
NORMANDY

MONT-
SAINT-MICHEL ■

DINAN ■  ■ DOL

■ RENNES

BRITTANY

# CHARACTERS

## William the Conqueror

I am the Duke of Normandy and I reign over a vast territory stretching from the Mont-Saint-Michel to the Somme Bay. I am Edward the Confessor's second cousin.

## Harold of Wessex

I am King Edward's brother-in-law, and the Earl of a rich region in the south of England. I have great influence over the entire nation.

## Edward the Confessor

I am named so thanks to my great piety. After spending my childhood in Normandy, I was crowned King of England in 1042. From my marriage with Edith of Wessex, I have no children.

EARLY ONE MORNING IN THE ROYAL PALACE OF WINCHESTER. THE SOUND OF CLOGS RESONATED IN THE COBBLED COURTYARD. TWO HORSEMEN HURRIED THEIR WAY TO THE VAST HALL WHERE KING EDWARD AWAITED THEM.

EDWARD SPOKE WITH A WEAK VOICE. HIS BROTHER-IN-LAW, EARL HAROLD, WAS INTRIGUED. HE APPROACHED AND LISTENED CAREFULLY.

Noble Harold, I am overwhelmed by old age. I have no heirs and I wish that England remain in peace after my death. I have decided to designate my cousin, William of Normandy, as my successor to the throne.

Your Highness, I will take to Normandy without delay, bearing this important message.

A LITTLE LATER, HAROLD AND HIS COMPANIONS MOUNTED THEIR METTLESOME HORSES AND HEADED FOR THE PORT OF BOSHAM IN THE SOUTH OF ENGLAND.

Thanks to William, Normandy is a rich region. He is sure to be a good king for our country.

This duke does not even speak Saxon. He is a stranger!

Harold is not of royal blood and the northern noblemen hate him...

But at least Harold is English. The people are fond of him.

WOOF WOOF

Let's stop at Bosham church. We shall pray to God for the successful accomplishment of our mission.

LATER, HAROLD HELD A FINE BANQUET IN HIS PALACE.

BUT SUDDENLY, A VIOLENT STORM BEGAN TO BREW. THE SAILS WERE FULL, THE BOATS WERE REELING, AND THE MEN WERE FRETFUL...

THANKFULLY, THE WINDS SETTLED IN THE EARLY MORNING.

BARELY HAD HAROLD SET FOOT ON THE SHORE WHEN A GROUP OF THREATENING HORSEMEN APPEARED FROM NOWHERE.

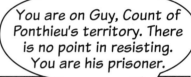

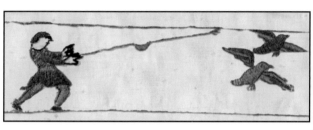

DUKE WILLIAM WAS INFORMED OF THE SITUATION IN HIS CASTLE IN ROUEN. FURIOUS, HE DECIDED TO TAKE IMMEDIATE ACTION.

Go and negotiate with Ponthieu for Harold's release.

AND BE QUICK!

NEGOTIATION PROVED TO BE TOUGH...

William demands that you free Harold. Immediately!

I shall receive no such orders from that illegitimate "duke"!

AFTER MANY LONG HOURS, GUY DE PONTHIEU FINALLY CONCEDED TO DUKE WILLIAM'S DEMANDS.

DUKE WILLIAM WAS DELIGHTED TO LEARN OF EDWARD'S MESSAGE.

BEFORE THEY LEFT, WILLIAM PROMISED HAROLD THE HAND OF ONE OF HIS DAUGHTERS, AELFGYVA.

Here's a slap so that don't forget your father's decision.

Let's go and pay a good lesson to Conan, the Duke of Brittany.

ON THE FRONTIER BETWEEN NORMANDY AND BRITTANY, THE MONT-SAINT-MICHEL ABBEY LOOMED OVER THE PASSING EXPEDITION.

BEWARE OF THE SINKING SAND!

YET, DESPITE THESE WARNINGS, THE MEN BECAME TRAPPED IN THE MUDDY SHORES. THANKFULLY, HAROLD SAVED TWO SOLDIERS - AN ENGLISHMAN AND A NORMAN.

Hold on!

THE BRETONS WERE SUBJECTED TO THE NORMANS' BITTER AND RELENTLESS ASSAULTS.

DINAN CASTLE WAS SET ALIGHT.

THE PUNITIVE MILITARY EXPEDITION WAS FINALLY VICTORIOUS.

AFTER THE BATTLE, WILLIAM HAD HAROLD KNIGHTED.

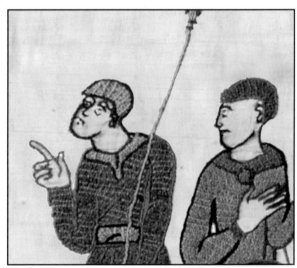

HAVING FULFILLED HIS MISSION, HAROLD RETURNED TO ENGLAND.

HAROLD WAS WELCOMED TO EDWARD'S THRONE ROOM.

THE CHURCH OF WESTMINSTER ABBEY WAS CONSECRATED LATE 1065.
KING EDWARD THE CONFESSOR CALLED HAROLD TO HIS DEATH BED.

A LITTLE LATER, KING EDWARD DIED AND HIS BODY WAS TRANSPORTED IN A SHROUD.

UNDER DIVINE PROTECTION, THE FUNERAL PROCESSION LED KING EDWARD TO WESTMINSTER ABBEY WHERE HE WAS BURIED.

Let us sing the praise of our pious king.

AFTER THE CEREMONY, THE SAXON LORDS GATHERED AROUND HAROLD.

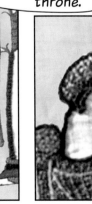

We have chosen you, for you are the most valorous of us all. You are worthy of the throne.

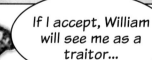

If I accept, William will see me as a traitor...

HAROLD NEVERTHELESS ACCEPTED AND TOOK THE THRONE. THE CEREMONY WAS HELD ON THE 6TH OF JANUARY 1066.

With this crown, sceptre and globe, I crown you King of England.

LONG LIVE KING HAROLD! HURRAH!

I'm sure he'll be an excellent leader!

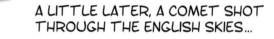

A LITTLE LATER, A COMET SHOT THROUGH THE ENGLISH SKIES...

Could this comet be the omen of an important event?

I had a worrying dream: a multitude of ships suddenly invaded the seas...

MEANWHILE, SAILORS BROUGHT NEWS OF HAROLD'S
CORONATION TO WILLIAM.

WILLIAM, WHO WAS IN HIS PALACE, WAS IMMEDIATELY INFORMED.

THE ENTIRE DUKEDOM IMMEDIATELY SET TO WORK.

Take heart! We have hundreds of them to fell!

Work hard and well! We will need to cross the Channel in these boats!

THE FLEET GREW AT GREAT SPEED...

BY THE SUMMER OF 1066, A VAST ARMADA WAS GATHERED IN THE DIVES ESTUARY.

IN JULY, THE SHIPS WERE LOADED UNDER THE SUMMER SUN: COATS OF MAIL, SWORDS, SPEARS, ARROWS, AXES, FOOD AND, OF COURSE, DRINK... HOWEVER, LATER, POOR WEATHER PREVENTED THEM FROM SETTING SAIL.

IN SEPTEMBER, THE ARMADA SAILED TOWARDS THE SOMME BAY, WHICH WAS CLOSER TO THE ENGLISH SHORES.

AFTER A LONG WAIT, IT FINALLY SET OFF FOR ENGLAND, UNDER FAVOURABLE WINDS.

EARLY IN THE MORNING, THE NORMAN ARMY LANDED ON THE BEACH AT PEVENSEY.

THE NORMANS SET TO REQUISITIONING LIVESTOCK AND FOOD SUPPLIES FROM THE VILLAGERS AROUND HASTINGS.

WILLIAM AND HIS TWO BROTHERS, ODO AND ROBERT, DISCUSSED THEIR BATTLE PLAN.

THE NORMAN CAMP BUSTLED WITH INTENSE ACTIVITY...

THE DUKE KEPT HIMSELF DULY INFORMED OF HAROLD'S EVERY MOVE.

Tell me spy, what news do you bring of the felon?

Harold is imposing intense training on his men in order to challenge us after his victory over Harald, the King of Norway!

Villainous Normans! I hope that Harold will exterminate each and every one of you!

My lord, seven thousand English soldiers are waiting in ambush on a hill just a stone's throw from here.

ACTION STATIONS!

ON THE MORNING OF THE 14TH OF OCTOBER 1066, DUKE WILLIAM SET OFF TO CHALLENGE KING HAROLD.

TOGETHER WITH WILLIAM, WE WILL BE VICTORIOUS!

How many of us will live to see the sunrise?

Tell me, Vital, do you know where Harold's army is?

Grouped together at the top of that hill. Let's go!

ON EITHER SIDE OF THE HILL, SAXON AND NORMAN SCOUTS WERE ON THE LOOKOUT.

THEY'RE COMING!

Noble King Harold, the Normans are as numerous as our own troops.

We will chase that pretentious duke from our land! After all, we beat Harald's scathing Vikings!

LONG LIVE WILLIAM! LONG LIVE THE FUTURE KING!

THE NORMAN HORSEMEN LAUNCHED THEIR ATTACK ON THE ENGLISH LINES.

THE ENGLISH FOOT SOLDIERS COURAGEOUSLY RESISTED THE NORMAN ATTACK. THE FIRST VICTIMS WERE STREWN ACROSS THE PLAIN.

* May God help us.

THE HEAVY AXES THE ENGLISH BRANDISHED WITH BOTH HANDS BROUGHT THE NORMAN ASSAULTS TO A HALT.

THE BATTLE WAS RAGING...

THE NORMANS RELENTLESSLY ADVANCED TOWARDS THE BITTERLY DEFENDED HILLTOP.

THE GROUND WAS SCATTERED WITH THE BODIES OF SOLDIERS AND HORSES.

WE WON'T CONCEDE AN INCH TO THE INVADERS!

SUDDENLY, A TERRIBLE RUMOUR TURNED THE NORMAN TROOPS' BLOOD COLD: WILLIAM WAS SAID TO BE DEAD...

DON'T LEAVE! KEEP FIGHTING!

Look here! I am not dead! Be brave and follow me!

The Duke's alive! He will lead us to victory.

34

IN A NEW LEASE OF LIFE, THE NORMAN HORSEMEN RELENTLESSLY ATTACKED THE SAXON FOOT SOLDIERS, WITH SUPPORT FROM THE ARCHERS.

THE ENGLISH DEFENCE WAS WEAKENING.

England will soon be William's!

THE BATTLE WAS NOT YET OVER, BUT WEAPONS AND CLOTHING WERE ALREADY PILLAGED FROM THE DEAD.

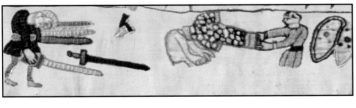

LATE AFTERNOON, THE NORMANS ATTACKED THE ROYAL GUARD. AT THAT MOMENT, HAROLD WAS STRUCK IN THE EYE WITH AN ARROW.

WILLIAM'S HORSEMEN IMMEDIATELY SET MERCILESSLY UPON HAROLD UNTIL HIS DEATH.

PANIC-STRICKEN, THE ENGLISH FLED THE BATTLEFIELD, PURSUED BY THE VICTORIOUS NORMANS.

This scene depicting the Saxon army in retreat, deprived of their chief, is the last one on the Bayeux Tapestry. The Normans, and their allies, were the great victors of the Battle of Hastings.

# THE END

WILLIAM THE CONQUEROR WAS CROWNED KING OF ENGLAND IN THE ABBEY-CHURCH OF WESTMINSTER ON CHRISTMAS DAY 1066.

THIS CONQUEST - OR RATHER INVASION, A GENUINE DIVINE JUDGEMENT, WAS TO BE THE LAST IN ENGLAND'S HISTORY.

# THE BAYEUX TAPESTRY,

## A PRECIOUS TESTIMONY OF ITS TIME

The Bayeux Tapestry is an 11th century masterpiece which has proved to be of exceptional documentary value towards our current knowledge of the period. When discovering the tapestry for the first time, the visitor can simply marvel at the great diversity of characters, clothes, buildings, ships and other features it portrays.

The following pages offer an insight into the secrets and the treasures it holds.

## CONTENTS

# THE HISTORY OF
# THE BAYEUX TAPESTRY

## COMPOSITION

The term "tapestry" generally refers more to a wall covering than to a woven cloth. As such, this term is often considered to be erroneous. For the Bayeux Tapestry was not created on a weaving loom, but was needle-embroidered on a linen cloth. The embroidery is divided into 3 parts almost throughout:

(1) The central, and the largest strip, tells the story of the conquest and includes text: a running commentary of events, character names, etc…

(2) The upper strip essentially represents more or less imaginary animals from Romanesque bestiaries.

(3) The lower strip depicts scenes from ancient fables (Aesop, Phaedrus), work in the fields…

## THE BAYEUX TAPESTRY, IN A FEW FIGURES:

68 metres (223 feet) long and 50 centimetres (1.6 feet) high
58 scenes: 33 of them in England (10 of the battle), 25 in France
8 colours of wool
623 characters represented
202 horses, 55 dogs, 505 miscellaneous animals
14 place names mentioned
37 buildings and 49 trees represented
200 coats of mail and 41 boats

# THE TAPESTRY'S CREATORS

Whereas popular tradition attributes Bayeux Tapestry's origin to Queen Matilda, historians agree on the theory that it was the Bishop, Odo who commissioned its embroidery.
The artist behind its illustrations, who was probably English, sought inspiration in 11th century manuscripts and in the period's traditional style. Needlework was performed by a team of embroiderers.

# GENEALOGY

**RICHARD I**
Duke of Normandy 942-996

**RICHARD II**
Duke of Normandy 996-1026

**EMMA (AELFGYVA)**
Queen of England 1002-1052

**ÆTHERELD II THE UNREADY**
King of England 979-1016

**GODWIN**
Earl of Wessex ✠1053

**ROBERT THE MAGNIFICENT**
Duke of Normandy 1027-1035

**HERLÈVE (ARLETTE)**
*successive unions*

**HERLUIN DE CONTEVILLE**
Viscount

**EDWARD THE CONFESSOR**
King of England 1042-1066

**EDITH**
Queen of England 1045-1075

**HAROLD II**
King of England 1066
(Earl of Wessex 1053-1066)

**WILLIAM THE CONQUEROR**
Duke of Normandy 1035-1087
King of England 1066-1087

**ODO**
Bishop of Bayeux 1049-1097

**ROBERT**
Count of Mortain ✠1091

# THE BAYEUX TAPESTRY'S CHRONOLOGY

**1077:** 14th July. Consecration of Bayeux Cathedral in the presence of King William, Queen Matilda, Odo Bishop of Bayeux and Lanfranc, the Archbishop of Canterbury. The tapestry was possibly already on display in the cathedral nave.

**1476:** The Tapestry is mentioned in an inventory of the cathedral's treasures, *"une tente très longue et estroicte de telle..."* (a long and narrow linen drape...)

**1728:** The prior of Saint-Vigor wrote of the continued custom of displaying the Tapestry in the nave of Bayeux Cathedral from St John's day to the first Sunday after the anniversary of its Consecration.

**1729:** The Benedictine monk Dom Bernard de Montfaucon presented the Tapestry in two of his works. His introductory text offered a fundamental resource for several generations of historians.

**1792:** Léonard Lambert-Leforestier protected the Tapestry when Revolutionaries sought to use it to cover a munitions cart.

**1804:** Napoleon Bonaparte had the Tapestry exhibited in the Louvre before returning it to the people of Bayeux.

**1842:** The Bayeux Tapestry was preserved and displayed in the Library, located Place du Château (bearing the number 1 on the library's list of manuscripts).

**1941:** It was studied by German scientists in Mondaye Abbey, then transferred to the Château de Sourches until 1944.

**1944:** The Tapestry was displayed once more in the Louvre, then returned to Bayeux in August 1945, where a new display was inaugurated in the Hôtel du Doyen in 1948.

**1983:** The Bayeux Tapestry was transferred to the former diocesan seminary, a vast edifice built in the late 17th century.

# IN THE MIDDLE AGES...

## FEUDALISM

As from the 10th century, the last of the Carolingian kings were incapable of defending their subjects. Consequently, major land owners gradually assumed the king's powers (justice, taxes…) to become great lords (dukes, counts, marquis…). They then conceded part of their land or fiefs to their best warriors who in turn became small lords. This is referred to as the feudal system (from the word "fief") or feudal society. The lord conceding land was the suzerain, and the receiving lord the vassal.

In a ceremony, referred to as "homage", the suzerain agreed to protect his vassal and the latter swore obedience and loyalty to his suzerain. Any vassal failing to respect his duties was considered as a traitor. On the contrary, a vassal could also withdraw from his obligations toward his lord, should the latter fail to fulfil his commitments. The feudal or vassalic link was extremely strong.

The rest of the population, including peasants, did not belong to the feudal society; they were dominated by and paid taxes to these "noble" lords.

KING

GREAT LORDS

SMALL LORDS

PEASANTRY

# CLOTHING

The Bayeux Tapestry offers but a limited view of civil dress during William the Conqueror's reign.

It depicts one unique representation of the various items of clothing worn by the Normans and the English: stockings (chausses), short breaches – generally hidden by a tunic – or bliaud – and a short mantle worn with a belt that covered the chest. In general, no headdress was worn. Long mantles were reserved for princes and ecclesiastics. Horsemen in civil dress generally wore a short mantle.

In the first part of the tapestry, most of the English soldiers have moustaches and thick hair to the rear of their heads. However, King Edward had a beard.

The Normans were shaven and the nape of their neck was bare.

### AELFGYVA

As a noble woman, she is wearing a bliaud. Over it, she is wearing a long robe with large sleeves. Her headdress covers her shoulders.
Just like lords, noble women wore wide mantles.

### WILLIAM

The Duke of Normandy is seated; he is bearing a sword in his right hand as a sign of his authority.

METAL FASTENER OR "FIBULA"

MANTLE

BLIAUD

CHAUSSES

SHOES

### COMBAT DRESS

Over their bliaud, noble knights wore a metal coat of mail, referred to as a hauberk and made of riveted and intertwined links. The front of the coat of mail was open to enable the knight to mount his horse. A total of around 30,000 links were needed to produce a single coat of mail!

# ON HORSEBACK!

The Bayeux Tapestry includes a total of 202 representations of horses, most of them stallions. These chargers were mounted by Norman horsemen; their harnessing was equivalent to present-day equipment. The English fought on foot, they were foot soldiers or infantrymen.

SPEAR — NASAL HELMET

SHIELD — REINS

CANTLE — LEATHER BRIDLE

SADDLE

BIT

POMMEL

STRAP

STIRRUP

SPUR

This Norman horseman is sitting on a saddle comprising a wooden frame covered with leather. The saddle is in turn placed on a rug laid on the horse's back and attached with a relatively large strap under its belly, and a further strap round its breast. The pommel and cantle are relatively high, in order to prevent the horseman from falling in the case of a sudden halt.

# BY BOAT!

The Viking longboat (wrongly referred to as a "Drakkar") is the ancestor of the Norman ship or "esneque". This shallow vessel required no harbour; it could be easily dragged onto dry land and left to rest on its keel. Equipped with an anchor, it could be rowed or sailed.

It was often adorned with both prow and stern figureheads - typically heads of imaginary animals: dragons, griffons… Each ship had a single mast placed in its centre with a very simple rig. The mast was mobile enabling it to be frequently raised or lowered.

For manoeuvres near beaches or the harbour, a boat hook was used (a long blade used to steer the boat by pushing down on the sea bed). When sailing in the high seas, shields were lined up inside the gunwale.

It is estimated that between 30 to 50 men could board each vessel, hence suggesting a fleet of at least 700 ships for William's expedition.

# PEASANTS

The border of scene 10 on the embroidery depicts peasants at work. They offer a fine illustration of 11th century agricultural advances.

MIGRATORY BIRDS WERE FREQUENTLY HUNTED USING A CATAPULT.

TECHNICAL IMPROVEMENTS: TOOLS MADE OF IRON RATHER THAN WOOD, WHEELED AND MOULD BOARD PLOUGHS, BREAST COLLAR FOR HARNESSING HORSES, WATER MILLS...

NEW LAND WAS PLOUGHED, HARVESTS WERE INCREASINGLY ABUNDANT, FAMINE LESS FREQUENT AND THE POPULATION SPREADING.

THE 11TH CENTURY MARKED THE DAWN OF A PERIOD OF MAJOR LAND CLEARANCE.

# MEALTIME

Although knives were used to prick meat, most diners ate with their fingers. There was no fork, for it was only invented in the 13th century. Wine or barley beer was drunk in metal or turned wooden cups. The English occasionally drank from animal horns.

Lordly meals generally comprised large quantities of meat: beef, mutton, pork and poultry, but also game: pheasant, heron, partridge, deer, wild boar, hare, rabbit and even bear...

Meat was a rarity for the humble, who occasionally ate pork. They ate dry, but rarely fresh fruit, and honey instead of sugar. They were familiar with neither tomatoes nor potatoes.
With flour made from wheat, oats or rye, peasants prepared bread, pancakes and porridge. Vegetables from the garden were used as a base for soup and broth.

Scene 43: William has just set foot on English soil. Bishop Odo, seated at the place of honour, blesses the meal. It's Friday, a day without meat for Christians, and the fish is placed in front of him.

# HOUSES

Peasant houses were generally low and with one single room. They had no windows. Depending on the region, walls could be made of planks or cob (a mixture of straw and clay), or even stone. The roof was thatched or covered with clay tiles, stone or shingle (wooden tiles).

Stone-worked fireplaces were soon to develop, but often a mere hole in the centre of the roof enabled smoke to be evacuated.

At night, animals such as cattle and sheep, slept inside the house, their presence offering extra heat. Peasants owned a few furnishings such as wooden stools, a table and a chest for clothes. The shared bed consisted of a straw mattress.

# CASTLES

From the 8th to the 11th century, successive waves of invasion had struck Spain, Italy and the Frankish kingdom. Protection was a priority. The kings and emperors offered their barons territories to defend. The latter built refuges, referred to as "motte castles". They were the very first fortified castles in history.

They were built by peasants who dug ditches, gathered heaps of earth to build the motte (or earthen mound) and carved stakes to form the stockade.

In front of the mound, there was a flattened area, the lower courtyard, where several buildings were erected: the lord's lodge, the chapel, the kitchens, the stables, the forge… From the top of the watch tower or keep, built on the mound, guards kept a look-out over the surrounding countryside. All of the aforementioned buildings were made of wood and were therefore easy to burn down if attacked.

Castles were built of stone as from the 11th century. The mound was generally abandoned, for the heavy keep required to be built on a flat and solid base, presenting no risk of collapse.

# HIDDEN MEANINGS...

## FABLES

The Bayeux Tapestry contains several allusions to fables dating back to the Antiquity. These fables were reproduced by Jean de la Fontaine in the 17th century.

**THE WOLF AND THE CRANE**

*LA LICE ET SA COMPAGNE*
(THE HOUND AND HIS MATE)

**THE WOLF AND THE LAMB**

**THE MOUSE, THE FROG AND THE HAWK**

**THE CROW AND THE FOX**

**THE MONKEY AS KING**

## THE COMET

In 1066, a shooting star was observed throughout Europe. It was the comet that was later to be named "Halley's Comet" after the British astronomer Edmond Halley (1656-1742) who had calculated its return for the winter of 1758-1759.

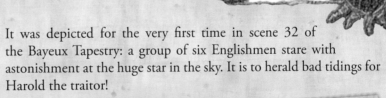

It was depicted for the very first time in scene 32 of the Bayeux Tapestry: a group of six Englishmen stare with astonishment at the huge star in the sky. It is to herald bad tidings for Harold the traitor!

In the year 837, the Emperor Louis I the Pious was panic-stricken before the sight of Halley's Comet and, although he died 3 years later, the appearance of the comet was associated with his death...
In 1759, the comet inspired many a hairstyle in Paris and the game "*Jeu de la Comète*", later to become "*Nain Jaune*" (Yellow Dwarf), was invented. In 1910, several people committed suicide when they learned of Halley's Comet's imminent return, convinced that it emitted mortal gases!

## "SLEIGHT OF HAND"

The creators of the Bayeux Tapestry offered its characters the power of expression via their different postures, in particular their arm and hand movements. These many hands, often portrayed larger than life, articulate and enliven the work, creating a genuine form of sign language.

PRAYER

MISSION

WARNING

DEMONSTRATION

DISCUSSION

Acknowledgements:
Produced in partnership with the Town of Bayeux.

15 rue de Largerie - 14480 Cully
Tel: 02 31 08 31 08
Fax: 02 31 08 31 09
E-mail: info@orep-pub.com

Web: www.orepeditions.com

# OREP
## E D I T I O N S

Editor: Philippe PIQUE
Graphic design: Éditions OREP
Graphics and layout: Arthur SHELTON
English translation: Heather COSTIL

ISBN: 978-2-8151-0050-2
Copyright OREP 2010
All rights reserved

Legal deposit: 3rd quarter 2010
Printed in the EC